British
Wildlife
Tales

What's that Coming Over the Hill?

words and pictures by Carl A. Mynott

What's that Coming Over the Hill?

for Mumsy
who literally made me
from scratch.

The tent is getting warmer now
the sun is shining through

a frying pan is sizzling
and the grass is damp with dew

Great rocky crags are sparkling
and the clouds have disappeared

The weather in the hills is now much
better than they feared

A shape appears above the ridge
and the little one stops still

Mummy, Daddy, tell me!
What's that coming over the hill?

Over the brow and in front of the sun
two tiny trees appear

A red deer stag has antlers
that look enormous when they're near

Their four long legs and short brown coat
help hide them in the trees

whilst foraging around the woods
to snack on fresh green leaves

Little one then hears a sound
they had never heard before

The awesome stag lifts up his head
and lets out a mighty roar

A kronking sound makes Dad look up
and sunlight hurts his eyes

The jet black shape soars through the air
a master in the skies

The raven is a great big bird
the biggest of the crows

A wedge-shaped tail and chunky beak
and shaggy feathered robes

It tumbles, turns and twists and dives
above the rocky towers

The family stands all rooted still
among the mountain flowers

'Mummy look! A blackbird'
it's flitting near those boulders

I need to get a better look
Can I sit up on your shoulders?

Mummy says that blackbird's strange
it has a different chest

This one has a patch of white
it's not like all the rest

Daddy says 'oh I know why
this one looks unusual

it's one that lives much higher up
it's really a Ring Ouzel'

The family turns and walks along
the little mountain trail

A pretty small bird flies ahead
with white upon its tail

Each time little one closes in
the tiny bird it flees

from rock to rock and stone to stone
It's always out of reach

The Wheatear's smart and stays ahead
He doesn't seem to rest

Then tempts you off along the path
to protect his rocky nest

Down below and in the glen
a ghostly bird sweeps by

then rockets up towards the sun
to dance up in the sky

It's feathers are both grey and white
with fantastic black tipped wings

It makes a cheeky chuckling sound
and hardly ever sings

Dad says "it's a Hen Harrier"
let's watch him swoop and dive

I think that he could really be
the most amazing bird alive

Climbing higher spots of snow
still lurk beneath the crags

The little one says can we stop
to sit down on our bags

One icy patch is touched by sun
Mum is dazzled by the glare

Dad yells out 'my goodness look!
a little mountain hare'

Its ears prick up and off it runs
as fast as it can go

to hide up on a frozen patch
with fur as white as snow

Out on the moor the heather blows
a sea of green and purple

Mummy jumps out of her skin
as a bird begins to hurtle

The red grouse chuckles as he flies
so fast above the ground

He wants to lead your eyes away
to stop his nest being found

He spies a tuffet far away
so clumsy when he stops

He settles down and starts to munch
on juicy heather tops

With the mountain peaks behind them now
they reach the glen at last

when a flash of brown darts up the stream
with wing-beats lightning fast

The Dipper sees the perfect rock
to hunt bugs that swim below

She picks her prey and in she pops
to grab the one that's slow

She clamps it tight inside her beak
and flies back up the burn

One lucky chick gets fed again
while the others wait their turn

The forest edge is different here
there's so much lichen in the trees

Out on the limbs of Scottish pines
a ginger mammal climbs with ease

With tufted ears, and fluffy tail
These are red, not grey

They're smaller than the ones back home
"and cuter too" Dad says

Tight in the Red Squirrel's clutch there is
a golden hazelnut

He puts those little teeth to work
and nibbles it all up

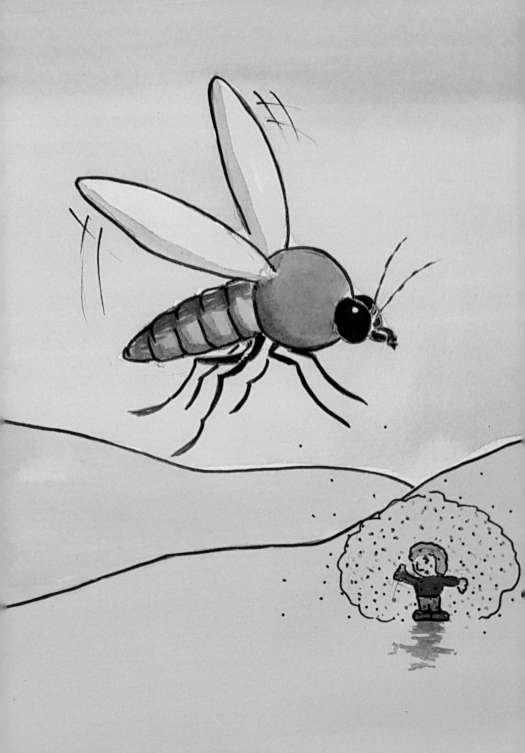

Back at camp the air is still
and calm as it can be

It's odd because there's no one out
Not a person to be seen

They're all zipped up inside their tents
for outside flies a pest

Dad says, 'quick, let's get inside
it's the safest place to rest'

'You'll soon wish you were back up high
still climbing on the ridge'

'for down here there's a trillion beasts
huge clouds of Scottish Midge!'

The sun has gone beneath the hills
as the family reach their camp

Mum pulls the zip, they climb inside
and Dad puts on the lamp

It's dark outside and getting cool
it's time to close the door

Little one sets out the tent
with cushions on the floor

Soon the pots are bubbling hot
and plates are being filled

They settle down to talk about
what came up over the hill

Help the grown-ups...

If the grown-ups are planning where to go
this summer holiday time

Tell them that you want a trip
with hills and peaks to climb

The road trip will be lots of fun
there's room for everyone

It may well rain, there might be wind
with luck there could be sun

So pack the tents, the sleeping bags
and lots of things to eat

Just think of all the amazing birds
and creatures you might meet

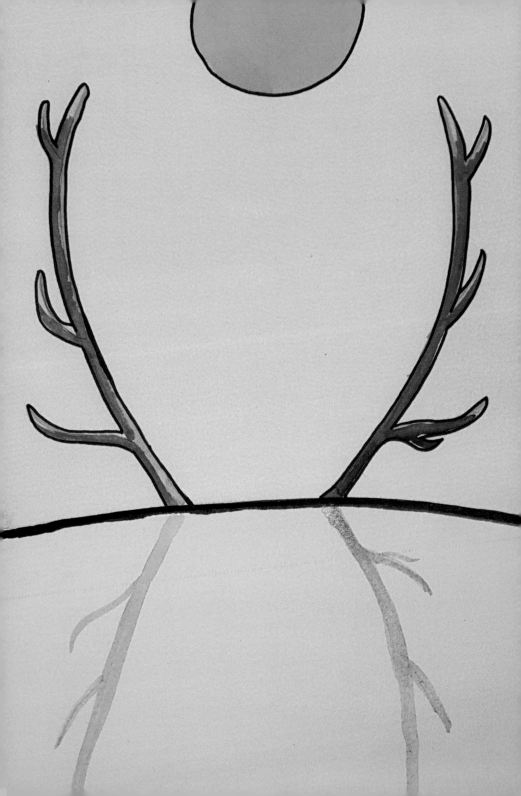

How to get up into the hills...

You'll need good shoes, a rainproof coat
a jumper and a map

Add food and drink and a compass too
don't forget a nice warm hat

Plan your route, or take a guide
make sure you don't get lost

Down in the glen it might be hot
but up high there could be frost!

Ask mum or dad to take a tent
in case there is a storm

So you can stop and take some shelter
where it's cosy and it's warm

Which creatures did you see coming over the hill?

Did you see a Red Deer? ◯

Did you see a Raven? ◯

Did you see a Ring Ouzel? ◯

Did you see a Wheatear? ◯

Did you see a Hen Harrier? ◯

Did you see a Mountain Hare? ◯

Did you see a Red Grouse? ◯

Did you see a Dipper? ◯

Did you see a Red Squirrel? ◯

Did you see a Scottish Midge? ◯

There are many things in life that are important

Two of them inspired me to begin creating these books

They are:

My family
and
the natural world

If you do just two things in life, do these:

Love your family
and
teach them about the natural world

You're already doing one of them...
Thank you for buying my book.

Carl x

BOOKS IN THE BRITISH WILDLIFE TALES SERIES

AVAILABLE NOW:
The Birds at the Bottom of the Garden
ISBN: 978-0-9929398-0-9

The Birds Down the Lane
ISBN: 978-0-9929398-1-6

What's in the Wood Pile?
ISBN: 978-0-9929398-3-0

What's that Coming Over the Hill?
ISBN: 978-0-9929398-4-7

COMING SOON:
What's that at the Seaside?
featuring 10 fascinating creatures that live around the coast of Britain

For more information, and for details about future titles, please visit the British Wildlife Tales website at:

www.britishwildlifetales.co.uk